Intr(

Welcome to the Study Guide to   I entirely
on the *'Words'* that I received from   y people
as possible, throughout all branche   n church,
may read, receive and act upon the__   io way do
I see these *'Words'* replacing or superseding the Bible. I believe we __ Jld regard
them as a blessing and a privilege. In them, God is giving us a peek into His heart,
mind and wishes.

Using this guide

The idea is that you will use this guide for group study, covering one section per week, over a six week period, possibly during Lent or Advent, adding extra weeks. It is an intensive six week course, or could be a more leisurely twelve week course, taking two weeks for each section.

Each section takes the *'Words'* clause by clause, set out in the shaded boxes, giving suggestions for meditation, discussion, activities and prayer, based on the *'Words'* and the Bible passages chosen to consolidate them.

It is assumed that each group member will prepare for each meeting by reading through the section in the week prior to the meeting and write their responses to the questions into the booklet, or in a notepad, or complete charts and tasks as found in the section. This is because there is a lot of material in each section and it would be difficult, if not impossible, to cover it if everyone had to think and pray about and then write down their responses at the meeting. The group can then give the maximum meeting time to sharing, praying over and discussing those responses and considering any action they need to take as a result.

There are suggestions for opening and closing prayer. These are offered as an aide, you do not have to use the exact words of the prayer. Feel free to use your own style of prayer and worship at these points. The final meditation, however, should form an integral and vital part of your meeting.

The timings and organisation of your meetings is, of course, for each group to decide, according to their partic- . ular constraints. The minimum time you would need for a meeting though, would be 2 hours.

1

Set One

"What I want"

Worship and opening prayer

Heavenly Father, as we start this study, we dedicate ourselves to You. Work deep within us to change the things that need changing and to bring out more of our true selves, as You made them to be. Send Your Holy Spirit to guide and direct all we do and to keep us on the straight path to You. Amen.

Key Bible Passage this week :-
1 Tim 2:1-8

A) **"I want to be the most important person in your lives."**
"I want mankind everywhere to lift up holy hands and worship Me."

Which songs, or Bible passages, can you think of on the theme of putting God first?

Which one do you think expresses this idea most effectively?

This set could be seen
as God's 'policy and
principle' statement.

To resolve this week:-
How should we respond,
as a church?

Look up Psalm 24:3-4 and Romans 12:1
How do we get clean hands and pure hearts according to the Psalmist?

How do these two scriptures tally?
Spend a little time meditating on them. Share any pictures or thoughts the two
of them bring to mind.

Name your church [for Churches together groups] or members of your church
hierarchy and pray for them, one by one.
Write post-it prayers on any issue from this study and stick them to a prayer
board.

B)   ***"I want all men to know My love, My care, My salvation."***
"I want to shower you with My blessings."

How do non-Christians sense or experience God's love?
[We will be looking at Christians knowing God's love next week.]

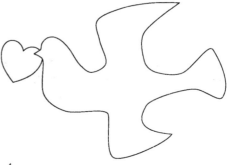

4

Think of 5 ways in which God has blessed you.
These could be material, physical or spiritual benefits.

1	
2	
3	
4	
5	

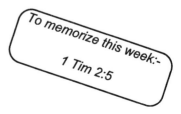

To memorize this week:-
1 Tim 2:5

C) *"I want My people to turn from their selfish, sinful ways, to turn back to Me."*
"I want to bless you, My people and be with you always, everywhere."

This *'Word'* is calling for repentance.
What do you understand by repentance?

What do you, personally, need to repent of?

•

•

•

Is there anywhere God cannot be with you?

Have you ever felt that God was not with you?

How was that resolved?

If it wasn't, what help would you like? Spend some time addressing each others needs here.

> ***D)***   *"I want to pour out My Spirit on you so that you can be My messengers, stewards and ambassadors in the world."*
>
> *"I want My church to reverberate with My praise and My power so that the world sits up and takes notice."*

Look at the little phrase 'so that', used in both these extracts.
What is it's implication?

What is the difference between a messenger, a steward and an ambassador?

Messenger:-

Steward:-

Ambassador:-

It seems we are being called to be all three here.
How do you see yourself in each of these three roles?

Define 'church' as you understand it.

What does the word reverberate mean?

To what extent does the church you attend reverberate?
Where could it do better?

Meditation

Theme - "I want to be the most important person in your lives."

You might find these helpful -
Psalm 8
Songs of Fellowship 27 "As the deer pants"

Closing Prayer

Heavenly Father, be the most important person in our lives. Help us when we drift away from You, when the urgent and strident demands of everyday living draw us far from You. Keep us close to You, filled with Your Holy Spirit and shining with Your love through-out our days, in Jesus precious name we pray. Amen

Set Two

"What I desire"

Worship and opening prayer

*Thank You Lord and Father for Your love
for us, unconditional and undeserved, but
so, so deep. Help us to open our hearts to
You now and always, to respond with all
our love as You long for us to do.
Amen.*

Key Bible
Passage this
week :-
Song of Songs

A)   **"I desire a romantic relationship with each one of you,
My children."**
**"I long to be as intimate with you as the very air you
breathe."**

Look at the 9 song titles used as section headings in Chapter 2 of the book
'No Other God'
Select the one you think best sums up how you see God's love.

This set of *'Words'* shows the
kind of relationship God longs to
have with each individual

To resolve this week:-
How should we respond,
as individuals?

This may be a new concept for you.
How does it make you feel? If you wish, share your thoughts with the group.

Those for whom it is not a new idea, share how you came to relate to God in this way. Be sensitive to each other, but open to allow God to work in your heart, mind and spirit, as He wishes.

B) *"I rejoice over you with singing, My delight is in you and you are desirable to Me."*
"I long to adorn you with the adornments of My love, with gifts and garments, graces and a new name known only to Me."

Look up Zephaniah 3:17

Take a few moments' quiet to let this scripture sink in, or speak to you, then share your reactions with the group.

I rejoice over you ♪ ♪ ♪ ♪ ♪ ♪

What would you say your gifts are? Share your thoughts and help others who are not so sure.

What do you understand by:-

Garments

Graces

A new name

To memorize this week:-

Song of Songs 8:6-7

> C)   *"I am an aggressive lover, pursuing you, My beloved children, across the plains of Earth and Heaven, seeking to save, redeem, protect and nurture you."*
>
> *"I am deeply hurt when you are indifferent to My love and careless of My affection."*

What are your reactions to this?

Is this an easy, 'safe' God?

What picture of Him does this give you?

Look up Revelation 2:4-5

'When have we been indifferent to Your love and careless of your affection Lord?'

Spend a few moments allowing the Lord to show you His answers to that question.

D)   *"I long for you to reject all your other lovers and to remember your first love for Me, so that I can gather you close into My arms and whisper My endearments to you ."*

"Above all else I desire you with all My heart and long for you to desire Me with all your heart."

Think of 5 words to describe your relationship with God;

-
-
-
-
-

What matters most in your life?

Define your 'other lovers'. What do you need to do in order to reject them?

Meditation

Theme - " Above all else I desire you with all My heart and long for you to desire Me with all your heart."

These may be helpful -
Psalm 23
Songs of Fellowship 1562 "This is the air I breathe"

Closing Prayer

Dear Lord, this has been a challenging study. Give us the courage to open our hearts wide to Your amazing love, and to respond with all our hearts, all our minds and all our souls. Lord we rest in Your arms and receive the love You long to pour out on each one of us.
Thank You, thank You so much.

"What I command"

Worship and opening prayer

Dear Lord, help us as we meet for another week. Fill us with Your precious Holy Spirit so that we can be honest and true to You. Help us to see, face up to and be prepared to alter those things that need changing in our lives. Amen.

Key Bible Passage this week :-
Exodus 20:1-17

A) *"I have said I want to be first in your lives, to be the most important person to you."*

"My command is that you have no other God but Me."

How is your week organised?

How much time do you give to God?

Draw up a chart similar to this, that tallies with your lifestyle. Fill in what you usually do in each time slot so that you can see what preoccupies you most and consider what changes need to be made to give God the priority He is calling for.

	6-12 a.m.	12-6 p.m.	6-12 p.m.	12-6 a.m.
Sunday				
Monday				
Tuesday				
Wednesday				
Thursday				
Friday				
Saturday				

This set outlines the quality of
response and behaviour God
expects of us, once we are His.

To resolve this week:-
What do we need to
change, individually?

What is God's status in your life?

How has this changed since starting this study?

> ***B)***   *"I have given you My word, the Holy Scriptures, and My Word, My Son Jesus Christ."*
> *"I expect you to obey them both, willingly and lovingly."*

God sent Jesus to die for us.
What is your understanding of this?

Look up Matthew 22:37-40
Obedience is not a concept we talk about in church very much these days. From what God is saying here, it is still necessary. What is your reaction to this?

To memorize this week:-
Matthew 22:37-40

C) *"I command you to keep yourselves holy, to keep your lives free from worldly taints, to live by My statutes, laws and decrees."*

"In this way the world will see who I am and will understand My message."

How do you maintain holiness in your life?

What prevents holiness?

The second statement here is given an entire Chapter in the book.
Why do you think this is?

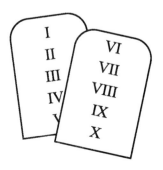

D) *"I do not want to frighten you or oppress you with harsh, impossible demands, as worldly masters do. I love you." "I am your Heavenly King and Master, there is no other God but Me."*

What is the difference between worldly demands and God's demands?

Find the 6 'I am' statements throughout the *'Words'*.
Look up John 8:58-59.
Consider what God is telling us through these statements.

> *E)*   *"My law is absolute, I made it, I alone, to achieve My purposes, none other, and it is good."*
> *"Walk in it and you will prosper and know peace."*

Have a bit of useful fun, completing the acronym:-

God's rule keeps us -

S

T

R

A

I

G

H

T

Put a Christian quality, habit or whatever occurs to you, starting with each of the above letters, eg 'Standing firm' for S

What is meant by 'prosper' here?

How do you know peace?

Read Job 42:7-17.
How did Job walk?

Meditation

Theme - "I delight in Your law"

These may be helpful -
Psalm 1
Songs of Fellowship 355 "Lord, how majestic You are."

Closing Prayer

Loving, Heavenly Father, thank You for leading us
through these studies. We commit to You all that
we have learnt and discovered about You and
about ourselves so far. We surrender our lives to
You, so that, through Your Holy Spirit, You can
make us the people You long for us to be.
In Jesus' precious and Holy Name. Amen

"What I ordain"

Worship and opening prayer

Lord and Father, You have made a wonderful world, full of Your glory. Forgive us that we have misused so much of it and taken it for granted. Forgive us for our selfishness in taking more than we need, more than a fair share of the world's resources. Most of all, Lord, forgive us when we do not share Your Gospel as freely as we might. In Jesus' Name. Amen.

Key Bible Passage this week :- Joel 2:28-32

A)   ***"My church .... to reflect My glory in the world."***

Look up Acts 2:41-47.
List the attributes of the church described here.

What were the outcomes of those attributes?

This set could be
said to be God's
'system'

To resolve this week:-
What kind of church do
we need to be?

> *"How little of My glory shines out from your churches. How much of your paltry glory masks My wonderful glory, when you pursue worldly ends instead of heavenly ones."*

How is the church actively pursuing heavenly ends?

How is the church pursuing worldly ends?

What can we do about that?

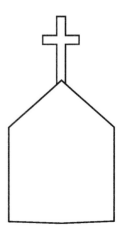

B) *"My people .... to share My love with the world."*

How can you, personally, share God's love with the world?

List 3 key purposes for the church.

•

•

•

To memorize this week:-

1 Peter 2:9

"Where are the prophets, teachers, evangelists and missionaries for this age?"

What would your answer to this question be?

What do you see as your mission for the Lord?

What inhibits you from carrying that out?

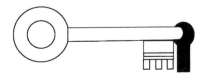

C)   *"My Son .... to bring salvation to the world."*

How do you answer people who say you cannot claim that Jesus is the only way to God?

"Why are you whispering when you should be shouting the Good News?"

Think of 5 ways to spread the gospel.

1

2

3

4

5

Which is your favoured way?

How can you gauge how effective it is?

Metaphorically, are you whispering or shouting?

> ### *D)*   *"My word .... to feed the hungry of the world."*

Define charity, mission and aid.

Have you got the right balance between mission, aid and charity?
How could you improve it?

"Why are you so preoccupied with the social when you should be focused on the spiritual?"

Does this imply we should not be involved in Aid etc?

How does your church set its priorities?

How could they be brought more in line with God's will?

E)   *"My creation .... to satisfy My love."*

How do you see this statement fitting in with the other four in this set of *'Words'*?

> *"How is it I look for the fulfillment of my creation and I do not see it?"*

What does God mean here?

How can we help fulfil His creation?

Meditation

Theme - "My creation to satisfy My love"

You may find these helpful -
Psalm 33:4-15
Songs of Fellowship 264 'I will build My church'

Closing Prayer

Gracious Father, we give You thanks for all that You have put in place to run this world. Empower us through Your Holy Spirit to work for You and with You in spreading the Good News wherever we go, for the sake of our Saviour Jesus. Amen

Set Five
"What I hate"

Worship and opening prayer

Heavenly Father, although we know You love us unconditionally, we also know that You love us with a tough love. A love that will not rest in its work of changing us into the people You long for us to be. A love that will not allow us to get away with things that ought not to be in our lives. We thank You that You do love us in this way and we surrender to You, to all You need to do in our lives. Amen.

Key Bible Passage this week :- Matthew 5:1-12

This is a 'problematic' set.
How do we reconcile it with the idea of a loving God?
Why is it important that we do make this reconciliation?
How does God help us achieve this, through what He says in the *'Words'*?

Look up Isaiah 55:9

This set covers six specific
things that are spoiling the
work of God's church.

To resolve this week:-
A healthy balance of negative
and positive thinking

A) *"I hate injustice. I am a God of mercy, requiring mercy.*
You know that I love all mankind, that I have made all
people equal. Any oppression or inequality is unjust and
offends against My good and perfect law."

We can probably all think of examples of injustice or oppression.
Briefly share these and consider prayerfully what you, individually, or as a
group, can do about them.

To memorize this week:-

Hosea 6:6

B)   *"I hate indifference. Too often you have been indiffer-*
ent to the sufferings of others, both near to you and far
off, but worse, far worse than this is your indifference to
Me, to My gifts, to My word and to My Spirit. Warm your
hearts, warm your spirits, fan into fire the flames of
passionate love for Me, for My Word and for My world."

Note the symmetry of the *'Word'* - Indifference for the world is cited first, then indifference to God, His gifts, His word and His Spirit.
Examine the last sentence in this *'Word'* to help you find the remedy for this. What comes first?

This *'Word'* calls for us to face up to our spiritual poverty.
Name 3 things that contribute to spiritual poverty.

Which of them are present in your life?

What do you need to do about this?

> C) *"I hate your compromises. My truth is absolute. I have made that clear to you. My word is founded on My truth. If you think you do not know what the truth is, then you need to know My word, to look for the truth, as I have given it to you, in Scripture. It is there, plain for you to see, but you do not look for it. You prefer to use the easy premises of the world, that are based on erroneous thinking. Read, learn , know and live My truth, and it will set you free, free from the tyrannous power of the world."*

How do you define compromise in this context?

In what ways are you, personally, compromising?

In what ways do you think the church is compromising?

Jesus used the phrase 'I tell you the truth' on many occasions.
Look up the following scriptures and write the key thought in each one.

Romans 1:25:-

1 Kings 17:24 :-

Psalm 51:6 :-

Daniel 9:13 :-

John 8:32 :-

What would you say their overall theme was?

Meditation

Theme - "Warm your hearts, warm your spirits, fan into fire the flames of passionate love for Me"

These may be helpful -
Psalm 51:1-17
Songs of Fellowship 58 Change my heart, O God

Closing Prayer

Dear Lord, help us by Your precious and wonderful grace, to amend our lives and bring them ever closer to what You want. We commit ourselves to living more and more for You and less and less for ourselves, in Jesus Name. Amen

Week 6

Set Five

"What I hate" (continued)

Worship and opening prayer

Loving, Heavenly Father, we offer ourselves to You once again as we come to study and learn from this final section of the 'Words'. Guide us Lord and fill us with Your Holy Spirit so we can learn what You want us to learn. Amen.

Key Bible Passage this week :- Matthew 5:17-20

D) **"I hate materialism. Take care that you have godly concern for the use of your money and possessions. Where I bless you with worldly wealth, I do it so that you can do more for Me. I do not give it only for your comfort and certainly not to confer superior status on you. I do it to enable you to spread My gospel and to proclaim My love to all the people I bring within your circle of influence, some very close to you, right where you are living, as well as others further away from you."**

What does the Bible say about money?

What is the difference between giving and tithing?

How do you use your money and possessions?

Discuss what your church [or denomination] is doing with its wealth, what it should be doing and how you could contribute to positive change.

What is your "circle of influence" ?

How can you share your faith in Christ within this circle?

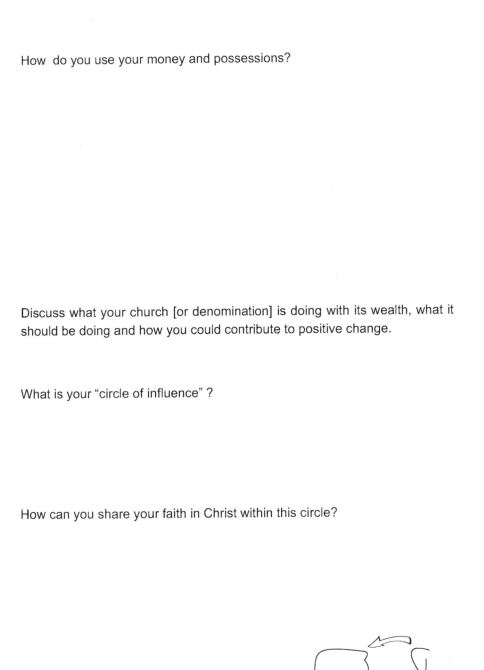

> ***E)***   *"I abhor hypocrisy, the whited sepulchre of religious pride, the sin that has beset and spoiled too much of the work of My church here on earth. I love to receive the praises of My children as they worship Me with hands and arms raised high, but why are so few of you willing to seek My forgiveness on your knees, even flat on your faces, so that I might forgive and raise you up to walk even more upright lives, pleasing and serving Me and fulfilling the deepest desires of your own hearts?"*

What characteristics of religious pride do you see within your own church?

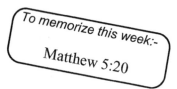

To memorize this week:-

Matthew 5:20

On what occasions do you praise God?

What do you need God to forgive in your life?
Prayerfully consider your response as individuals. Then carry it out. You may like to write your sins on cards and burn them as part of your final celebrations.

What is the reward God is offering to us here?

F) *"I hate defeatism. My church is The Church triumphant, victorious. I am not dead, Christianity is not dead. I am very much alive and My followers have life, abundant life, and joy, deep wells of joy, bubbling up in their spirits, bubbling up and spilling over, out into the world around them. Spilling out and always being refilled, refilled from the never-ending source that is Me. How can you walk in defeat when I have given you feet to skip lightly in blissful joy through this life and all its troubles? Shake off your feeling of defeat My children. Lift up your heads, lift up your eyes and see My triumph, see My victory and know that we can never, never be defeated.*

Amen, so be it. As I have spoken, so shall it be. Halleluiah!"

Meditation

With this final 'Word' please meditate on and memorise it and then follow on by answering the questions below.

Why does God hate defeatism?

How can you obtain this abundant life and deep joy?

Where is the source of all this power?